PUBLISHER'S NOTE

We had a secretary here, briefly, who answered the phone one day when Walt Kelly was calling and said in a sprightly voice, "Yes, Mr. Kelly, is it about anything?"

The same question could be applied with effect to the great majority of the 12,000 books published this year in America.

Trying it on with this one, the answer appears to be, if you are in Congress or a lawyer, in the affirmative. Otherwise, yes. It isn't about everything, just some things. That's why it is called The Incompleat Pogo. The Compleat Pogo will have to wait for a few thousand years when we know the answers to everything instead of just getting around, as we are now, to a foggy idea of what some of the questions are.

The
INCOMPLEAT
POGO

by
Walt Kelly

SIMON AND SCHUSTER
NEW YORK

THIRD PRINTING,

MANUFACTURED IN THE UNITED STATES OF AMERICA
PRINTED BY WILLIAM KONECKY ASSOCIATES, INC., N. Y.
BOUND BY F. M. CHARLTON COMPANY, N. Y.

For my father

The poets have muddied all the little fountains.
Yet do not my strong eyes know you, far house? . . .

Antara, 6th century.

CONTENTS

CHAPTER
1

From Here On Down It's
Uphill All The Way

IF YOU GONNA PLAY *FAIR*, YOU IS GOTTA BE BLINDFOLDED OVER THE *BYEBONES*....*NOT ON THE MUSH!*

'LONG AS YOU CAN'T SEE WITHOUT YO' GLASSES, O.K.

YOO HOO

YES?

IT'S *ME*, GOOD OL' SEMINOLE SAM. I GOT A NEW LINE OF GOLDEN OPP-ORTUNITIES FOR OLD AN' YOUNG.

YOUR FRIEND HERE IS IN A *EXCELLENT* STATE TO GIVE MY PRODUCTS A *NOBLE* TRIAL.... A *BLINDFOLD* TEST OF PERIODICALS.

WE'LL TRY HIM OUT ON *COMIC BOOKS* FIRST.....*RIFFLE THRU THAT*, SIR.....*IT IS ALIVE WITH CHUCKLE*, *PERIL, AND FLAMING LOVE*------.*SAVOR ITS CRUNCHY GOODNESS, FRIEND......WEIGH ITS LIVELY MEATINESS....*

IT SOUND JES' FINE.

WUILL....IF I *GOTTA* CHOOSE, I THINK MEBBE *THIS* ONE'S FUNNIEST.

HA! NOW I'LL WARRANT YOU IT'S THE BRAND WHICH *I* ADVOCATE----....*YES, CLASS WILL TELL----*

OOP! SORRY! MISTAKENLY, I HANDED YOU *MY* COPY OF THE *CONGRESSIONAL RECORD.* OUR FACTORY IS CONSIDERING ILLUSTRATING IT IN COLOR----PANEL BY PANEL...*EXCELLENT CHOICE, BUT NOT READY*....COME, LET'S TRY AGAIN, SIR.

Our Hero Dots One Eye
and Crosses The Other,
Hand Over Hand

19

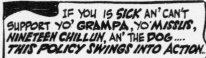

IF YOU IS *SICK* AN' CAN'T SUPPORT YO' *GRAMPA*, YO' *MISSUS*, *NINETEEN CHILLUN*, AN' THE *DOG* .... *THIS POLICY SWINGS INTO ACTION*..

'A DOCTOR COMES IN AN' *PATCHES* YOU UP...'FORE YOU KNOWS IT, YOU IS *UP* AN' ON YO' WAY *BACK* TO WORK!

I *KNOWED* THERE WAS A *CATCH* IN IT!.

YOU GOTTA THINK OF THE *FUTURE*, SIR ... DON'T YOU EVER PLAN FOR A *RAINY DAY*?

NO, I USUAL LETS 'EM COME 'LONG BY THEY SELFS.

YOU IS IMPROVIDENT. HOW CAN YOU TELL WHAT THE DAY AFTER TO-MORROW MAY BE?

IF IT'S ANY-THING EXCEPT *JAN. 28*, I IS GONNA WRITE A *NASTY* LETTER TO THE CALENDAR COMPANY.

MY DEAR SIR, *WHY DO YOU NOT WISH TO PLAN FOR A RAINY DAY*?

AW, THEY AIN'T NO USE IN *THAT*, SAM... I PLANS ON NOTHIN' BUT THE *BEST* ..... *SUNSHINE* AN' FOUR SQUARE MEALS A DAY....

THE S.S. COLIN HAWORTH

THE *GUMMINT* NEEDS A MAN LIKE YOU IN THE *RAINY DAY DEP'T.*

I IS *GUMMER-MENTAL TIMBER* I ALLUS SAY.

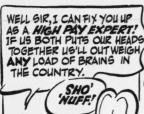

Panel 1: WELL SIR, I CAN FIX YOU UP AS A *HIGH PAY EXPERT!* IF US BOTH PUTS OUR HEADS TOGETHER US'LL OUTWEIGH **ANY** LOAD OF BRAINS IN THE COUNTRY.

SHO' 'NUFF!

Panel 2: IF YOU TWO IS GONE PACK SUCH HEAVY BRAINS ON A BOAT RIDE, YOU MOUGHT AS WELL DO A LI'L' OAR WORK....

THE S.S. COLIN HAWORTH

Panel 3: I IS CARRYIN' THE *LUNCH...* YOU S'PECK ME TO DO *EVER'THIN'?*

Panel 4: I FINDS YO' DISCUSSION 'BOUT *ME* HAVIN' **GRADE** A BRAINS A EXTREMELY *FAST-AN'-ATIN'* CONJECTURE, SAM.

Panel 5: THE **RAINY DAY** DIVISION OF THE WEATHER BUREAU CAN USE A MAN LIKE YOU, ALBERT.

THE CITY OF LOSANTIVILLE

Panel 6: THE COUNTRY CALLS ME, HUH?

AYE, THE *CLARION* VOICE OF STAR STRIPED DUTY SOUNDS *E'EN* NOW.

Panel 7: *DAWG BONE!*

DAWG BONE, INDEED, AS YOU SO *APTLY* PUT IT, SIR... FOR ALL *TOO* LONG, WE'VE TOOK OUR *WEATHER* FROM **CANADA** ....OR FROM SOME SUCH PLACE *OUTSIDE* THE BELOVED BORDERS OF OUR OWN LAND.

Panel 8: WHY'S WE GOT TO IMPORT OUR WEATHER?... AIN'T US ABLE TO COOK IT UP OURSELFS?

HEY!

THE CITY OF LOSANTIVILLE

Panel 9: BUT OF *COURSE!* HONEST, NATIVE WEATHER CAN BE BUILT ANYWHERE! *IN CINCINNATI* FOR EXAMPLE.... THE "GARDEN OF THE OHIO."

21

22

CHAPTER
3

Weather Forecast:

Tiara Boom-De-Ay In

The Afternoon

24

CHAPTER
4

Mole Blooms
In A Spray Of
Myopia

30

31

YOU MEAN "EXAGGERATION." AWK!

I KNOW WHAT I MEAN.

I'M NOT *SO* NEAR SIGHTED BUT WHAT I'D OF *NOTICED* IT IN THE MIRROR IF I HAD DIED. HOW?

YOU'RE JUST IN TIME, MOLE... OL' SAM IS SELLIN' ALBERT THE *CINCINNATI* POST BUILDIN'... ALBERT'S GONE USE IT FOR A *WEATHER FACTORY*.... TO MAKE GOOD U.S. AN' A. TYPE OF WEATHER.

EXCELLENT IDEA... WE NEED *BETTER* WEATHER THAN CANADA'S BEEN SENDING US..... *THEIR* EXPORT WEATHER IS SHODDY! *SHODDY!*

SLEEZY STUFF IN WINTER... NO *BODY* TO IT.....WEARS THIN IN *NO* TIME.....AND THEIR SUMMER STOCK IS LAUGHABLE (*HA HA*)...AN INTERNATIONAL *FRAUD!* TAKE THE GULF STREAM... ....*HAH!*

AIN'T THE GULFSTREAM OUR OWN JOB?

I'D ADVISE YOU TO WASH YOUR MOUTH OUT WITH SOAP, DEAR BOY.....*THAT* STREAM IS FROM THE GULF OF *MEXICO!* HAH! ABSOLUTELY UNREGULATED...! WANDERING *WILLY NILLY* ALL OVER OUR SOVEREIGN OCEAN .... A *SCANDAL!*

JUST ONE QUESTION, MY SON. *WHY* IS ALBERT GOING TO MANUFACTURE WEATHER IN A *FOREIGN* CITY.....? CINCINNATI *INDEED!* WHY GO TO GREECE?

CINCINNATI AIN'T OVER IN GREECE.

DON'T USE *AIN'T*...WHEN I SAY: *IS*... AN' STOP PICKING ON AN OL' MAN WHAT CAN HARDLY SEE! A CIVIL TONGUE, YOUTH, A *CIVIL* TONGUE!

COULD IT *BE* THAT YOU'RE *AFRAID* TO ANSWER? PASS THE FISH, LAD.... *BRISKLY DOES IT.*

HE PICKED CINCINNATI 'CAUSE IT'S THE PLACE WHAT GOT A VERY FINE MEAN TEMPERATURE

MEAN, *EH?* THAT'S THE *FLIMSY* TYPE WE BEEN GETTING FROM *CANADA*...A CARTEL, NO DOUBT, OF *INTERNATIONAL ALLIGATORS*...PASS THE BOTTLE OF CHUTNEY, BOY...

US DON'T 'LOW NO DRINKIN' TYPE LICKER IN HERE, MOLE.

NO *CHUTNEY?* ACK! IN THAT CASE, I'LL NEED ANOTHER FISH.. ...A CRISPY GOLDEN BROWN ONE ...

YOU ET 'EM ALL.

A SHAME! YOU DIDN'T EVEN SAVE *ONE* FOR YOUR GOOD COMPANIONS... MR. FOX OR MR. ALLIGATOR? *VERY THOUGHTLESS, YOUNG MAN!*

HEY.

BUT YOU WAS HUNGRY.

37

38

39

CHAPTER
5

Wherein Our Hero Learns
That Hospitality Is
Merely Mortal

41

42

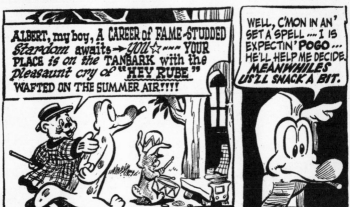

44

CHAPTER
6

Brains From Far And Wide
Are Summoned To Ponder
A Suicide Pack

PLOCK!

A **BOOBY TRAP!** IF I DIN'T OF SEED IT MYSELF I WOULD OF THUNK I COULDN'TNA B'LEEVE HE WOULDA OF DOOD IT HIS-SELF 'LESS I SAWN HE REAL MUS' OF DID DO IT WITH MY OWN EYES.....

WITH THIS *GARBAGE* HANGIN' OUTEN MY BAG, FOLKS'LL THINK I DON'T KNOW HOW TO *PACK!* ----I'LL GO BACK IN AN' *CLIP OFF* THE *HANGOVERS.*

OW! DAG NAG THAT POGO.....I FERGOT 'BOUT HIM HAVIN' THAT *MISSIN'* DOORSTEP!

OR----UM, LET'S SEE... I FERGOT 'BOUT HIM *NOT* HAVIN' A MISSIN' DOOR-STEP...

STILL HOW COULD HE *NOT* HAVE IT IF HE *DO* BUT HOW COULD HE *DO* IF----*YAWK!*

BY JING! HE DOGBONE WELL BETTER GIT IT FIXED! GOT IT OR NOT!

49

50

I ASK **CLIPPED** QUESTIONS, SIR----IF THE DOG'S GONE HE'S MISSIN' OR DEAD? WHO? WHICH?

I DUNNO! *EVER'BODY* WAS **NUTS** ABOUT HIM.

THE CASE IS BLOCKED! *"EVER'BODY WAS NUTS!"* THAT PART OF THE REPORT MAKES ME THINK! *AS A COP* I'M THROWIN' EVERY BRAIN IN MY HEAD INTO THIS.

AS LONG AS WE'RE **SHORT HANDED** I'LL GO GET **HELP!**

HEY, HOUN'DOG, C'MON AN' *HELP!* SOMETHIN' MUST IS HAPPENED TO *PUP DOG.* I LEFT HIM TIED UP... COULD YOU SNIFF OUT THE TRAIL?

GLADLY AN' IN DUTI- BALLY.

ALBERT STOPS BY..SEES I LEFT OL' PUP TIED TO THE DOOR STEP----ALBERT PICKS UP A SUITCASE... *PFFFT!* THE PUP IS **GONE!**

HAS OL' ALBERT STILL GOT THE GRIP?

NO, JUS' A LI'L' COUGH... HE FEEL JUS' FINE.

NO MORE OF THAT! THAT IS, IF YOU WANTS MY KEEN NOSE ON THE JOB... STUFFED THO' IT IS WITH *PNEUMONIA.*

YOU DON'T SMELL AS GOOD AS YOU DID?

GROWL.

CHAPTER
7

The Case Is Open
And/Or Shut At Will

ALL RIGHT, SIR, *THE CASE IS OPEN FOR BUSINESS AGAIN --- WHO WAS THE LAST TO SEE THE VICTIM?*

YOU WAS!

MAKE A NOTE OF THAT, SARGE: Time: 9:06 Remarks: *Last one to see the victim was you.*

NOT *ME!*

YEAH, NOT HIM; YOU!

CHANGE THAT TO: THE DOG IS DESCRIBED AS FOLLOWS:

NAME............?
AGE............?
HAIR............?
COLOR............?

?

IF HE AIN'T HERE WE WON'T KNOW ALL THAT 'TIL HE'S FOUND.

SO FAR WE KNOW THIS: *It's 9:06; your name is Albert.*

WE BETTER START *OVER....* IT'S 10:17 NOW---- THROWS THE CASE INTO A COCKED *HAT!*

WE'LL PLUG AWAY.

CLOSE THE CASE WHILST WE GO OVER THE *FACTS,* CHIEF.....*The pup dog's gone!* Your name: *Albert* Time: *10:17*

CHECK.

CHECK! NOW LET'S *SIFT* IT, CHIEF! THERE'S THE *CLOCK,* STOPPED AT *10:17* ON THE NOSE--- AND *THERE'S YOU!*

ME? THAT'S *ME!?*

54

CHAPTER
8

BRains, Size 6¼, Are
Pooled To Form A Shallow
But Slippery Puddle

Panel 1: WELL, *TIME 1:00!* I'LL REOPEN THE CASE... NOW, WHO DO YOU SUSPECT, OWL?

OL' MOLE! *THAT'S WHO!*

MOLE?

Panel 2: YESSIR, *HIM!* YOU NOTICE HIM SNOOPIN' AROUN'? *OH,* HE GOT A *BAD* NAME.... *HE* AIN'T UP TO *NO* GOOD... AN' *WHAT'S MORE....*

Panel 3: I SAID TO HIM: "*SEED THE PUP DOG?"* I SAYS... AN' *HE* SAYS: "*WHO?"...* *HA!* WHO INDEED!.. *HE DODGED!* AN' ALL THE TIME HE GOT THAT *SNEAKY LOOK* IN HIS EYE.

Panel 4: WHICH EYE WAS THIS HERE *SNEAKY LOOK IN,* SIR?

ALL OF 'EM!

IN ROUND NUMBERS HOW MANY WOULD YOU SAY? AT *A ROUGH GUESS?*

Panel 5: *MAN!* I IS *WORED OUT!* TROMPIN' ALL OVER THE SWAMP AN' NARY *HIDE NOR HAIR* OF THE PUP.

Panel 6: *HEY!* IS YOU SEED ANYTHIN' OF OL' *MOLE* WHILE YOU WAS OUT LOOKIN' FOR THE *PUP DOG?*

Panel 7: *NOPE!* WE DIN'T SEE THE PUP AN' WE DIN'T SEE *MOLE,* NEITHER.

ADD THAT UP, PARDNER. **TIME 1:12**...Remarks: *Both the Mole and the pup Wasn't seen.*

IN OTHER WORDS: TOGETHER, THEY IS **MISSIN'**!

CHECK! AN' YOU CAN ADD, (TIME 1:13½) *The Mole ain't tole talkin'*

THE WAY **EVIDENCE** IS PILIN' UP, *IT IS POSITIVELY UNCANNY!*

IT'S SURE TOO DEEP FOR ME.... I NEED MY BOOTS.

I THINK ALBERT AN' BEAUREGARD ARE ON THE **RIGHT TRAIL** ....IT LOOKS LIKE OL' MOLE DID IT ALLRIGHT.

DID WHAT?

SNATCHED THE **PUP DOG** OF COURSE...... HE'S PROB'LY A UNDERCOVER DOG CATCHER.

YOU AN' ALBERT AN' THE HOUN'DOG SURE BEEN **TALKIN'**!

YES, INDEED! WE'VE **DIS**-CUSSED, **RE**-CUSSED..... ALL WAS GIVE A FAIR CHANCE TO TALK AN' DEE-FEND MOLE --- BUT WE ENDED UP SUSPECTIN' HIM FAIR AN' SQUARE----

DID YOU HAVE TIME TO THINK?

ALL IN GOOD TIME .....WE AIN'T THE SLOPPY KIND WHAT TRIES TO DO **TWO** THINGS AT ONCE. *UP TO **NOW** WE BEEN JES' TALKIN'*...BUT WHEN WE START *THINKIN'* 'BOUT THIS.. *STAND BACK!*

JES' SO YOU DON'T FERGIT IT.

61

62

66

'LONG AS YOU TURNS OUT NOT TO BE *MOLE*, I GUESS WE DON'T WHACK NOBODY.

YEAH.... HOUN'DOG YOU IS A *SPOIL-SPORT.*

IT'S A GOOD THING I PACKED SOME OF YOUR **GRUB** IN YOUR BAG WITH *YOUR* TRAVELIN' CLO'ES FOR ME, POGO, 'CAUSE *I* IS WORKED UP A **APPETITE**....

QUITE SO.

JUS' THE SAME, MOLE, IF I HAD MY WAY, WE'D SHAKE A **CONFESSION** OUTEN *YOU!* --- I STILL THINK *YOU* STOLE THAT *POOR LI'L* --

-- PUP DOG.

DID YOU PUT ANY LIVERWITCH IN ...?

YOU PACKED LUNCH RIGHT IN WITH SOCKS AN' ALL ?

LOOK! ALBERT, YOU PACKED THE *PUP DOG* INTO THE *SUITCASE* --- **THAT'S** WHERE HE IS BEEN ALL THIS TIME!

AN' I 'THUNK HE WAS AT *DEATH'S DOOR* ... AW, THAT DEAR LI'L FELLA, *I* WOULDN'T WANT ANYTHIN' TO HAPPEN TO *HIM!*

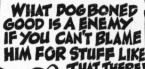

A Medium Rare Day
In June Is Well Done

IT'S A JUMPY WAY OF LIFE, ANYWAYS.

I BEEN FIGGERIN' OUT WHAT YOU SAID---THAT WE AIN'T GOT NO *FIFTY FIRST* OF *OCTOBER*.

WHAT'S TO FIGGER OUT 'BOUT *THAT*?

ALL THE *FIFTY FIRSTS* OF *OCTOBERS* FALL ON THE *TWENTEETHS* OF NOVEMBERS.

OCTOBER STOP ON THE THIRTY ONE OF IT.

WHY?

YOU CAN'T GO HAVIN' A WHOLE *YEARFUL* OF OCTOBER.

WHY NOT..? IT'S A *PERTY* MONTH.... WE COULD HAVE OCTOBER, CHRISTMAS, THE FOURTH OF JULY AN' MY BIRTHDAY AN' LET ALL THE OTHER MONTHS GO .... FEBRUARY FOR INSTINCT... *WHO* NEEDS IT?

72

A Friend Is Drunk
On A Sobering Note

IF YOU IS A *PERFESSIONAL* PREE-DICTER WHERE'D YOU PREEDICK AT AFORE?

I WORKED FOR A *NEW ORLEANS* NEWSPAPER.

H₂O

I WAS THE ORIGINAL *PICAYUNE FROG..* A WEATHER EXPERT...BUT THE BOSS, HONEST GEORGE, WAS A *HARD MAN*...MADE ME WEAR SHOES...SAID I WAS SOGGY AN' HE DIN'T LIKE HIS CARPETS ALL DAMPED....*THIS*, OF COURSE, MADE MY FEET HURT....

H₂O

NATURAL, I PREDICKS *RAIN* FOR *SIXTY SEVEN DAYS*...OL' GEORGE SAT AT HIS DESK UNDER A UM-BRELLA AN' CARRIED A LOADED LIGHTNIN' ROD AT ALL TIMES .... *WELL*, SIR! WE HAD SIXTY SEVEN DAYS OF *UN*-MITIGATED SUNSHINE ....

HONEST GEORGE PEEKS OUT AN' HE *SEE* : SOMETHIN' IS WRONG. HE TOOK BACK THE COMP'NY SHOES, GUV *ME* THE SACK AN' BRUNG IN ANOTHER BOY...WHO *KNOWS*, MEBBE A RELATIVE ... BUT ANYWAY A IMPOSTOR WHO COULDN'T PREDICK X̱MAS ON DEC. 24.

THAT IS OCTOBER 457th.

THIS NEW ORLEANS PAPER HELD A CONTEST TO SEE WHO'D BE THE WEATHER MAN... ME OR A OUTLANDER NAMED "POGO" (SAID TO HAVE SHARP WEATHER EARS.)

HA! ME AN' OL' GEORGE, THE HEAD MAN, FIXED *THAT!* WE BOLSTERED THE BALLOT BOX AN' I WAS A *SHOO IN!* .....ONLY LATER DID I LEARN THAT THE JOB CARRIED NO SALARY.

I DENOUNCED THIS PENURIOUS ATTITUDE AND FOUND MYSELF AT *LIBERTY*...SO I PICKETED THE MARDI GRAS SINGLEHANDED... *GEORGE* CHARGED THAT I WAS NOT A *FROG* BUT A MIDGET *ALLIGATOR!* A VILE SLANDER **!**

ON **WHO**, HOPPY TOES ?

WHAT'S IN THE SATCHEL, YOU **SHORT** TAILED SALAMAGANDER?

I WOULDN'T TELL ANY OVERGROWED LIZARD....

NOTHIN' BUT WATER...

I COME OVER TO SET UP A FORECASTIN' BUREAU.....

HAW.... I'LL JES' DRINK IT UP... I'LL LEARN HIM TO BE SO SMART.

I GOT A AMOEBA IN WATER... HE KNOWS *EVER'THIN'*

HE FORECASTS WEATHER AN' ...*HEY! YOU POT-EYED PLATTER-PUSS!* YOU DRUNK MY **FRIEND!**

76

CHAPTER
11

Owl Goes
Slumming

I KNOW YOU IS A BUSY MAN, MR. PICAYUNE HOP FROG, BUT HOW COME YO' A-MOEBA HAS H·2·O ON HIS LI'L' SATCHEL?

IT'S HIS 'NITIALS.

Y'SEE, I GOT ME A JOB BEIN' ADVANCE MAN FOR A PELICAN FROM UP BATON ROUGE WAY.... HE'S IN SHOW BUSINESS SO HE TELL ME: "GIT ON OUT WITH THE ALL SEEIN' AMOEBA WHAT KNOWS ALL AN' RUSTLE UP CROWDS..."

OL' AMOEBA GOT A NAME ON HIM WHAT SHOW HE KNOW ALL FROM BEGINNIN' TO END... YES SIR! HALPHA 2 OMEEBA... KINDA OF A CARNIVAL A-RAB.... 2 IS FOR TWO'S DAY... HIS BIRTHDAY BEIN' THE SECOND DAY OF THE WEEK.

THOUGHT TUESDAY WAS THE THIRD DAY OF THE WEEK.

NO, YOU'RE THINKIN' OF THIRD'S DAY...COMES AFORE FRIDAY.....DON'T FEEL BAD, THO', 'TAIN'T NO DISGRACE TO BE STUPID.

WHAT'S THE STORY 'BOUT THIS PELICAN?

MUS' OF IS START WAY BACK, MAN, GO BY NAME OF NAPOLEUM, HE COME 'LONG AN' HE SAY TO TH' PELICAN, HE SAY, "BOY, HOW YOU LIKE TO BUY LOU'SIANA?"

HEE! HE MUS' OF TOLE NAPOLEUM "GO BACK THAT FLITTER-FLY HOUSE." HE COULDN'T OF BOUGHT LOUISIANA.

HE DID TOO BOUGHT IT! INCLUDIN' NORTH AN' SOUTH DA-KOTA!

CHAPTER
12

An Affair Of Honor
Is An
Inside Job

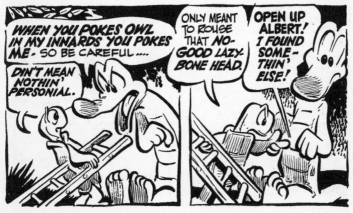

86

CHAPTER
13

The Hose Is Carried
To Extremes

90

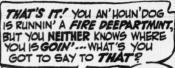

CHAPTER
14

In Which It Is Seen
That It Is Hard To Hold
As Much As A Pelican

PHOO--ALL IS LOST.

LOST MY AMOEBA *WITH* THE *GOLD* TOOTH---LOST MY SATCHEL AN'----

AN'-

AN' LOST YO' *JOB*, PICAYUNE! A *FINE ADVANCE MAN* YOU IS BEEN FOR *ME!*

ROOGEY BATOON! THE UNDENIABLE *PELICAN!* THE MAN WHO *MADE* THE LOU'SIANA PURCHASE...

HOW'D *YOU* DO IN THAT *CALAVERAS* COUNTY JUMP, CHAMP?

THEY THREW A *RINGER* AT ME..... A NON-GUILD MEMBER... HARDLY A FROG A· *TALL!*

I HAPPEN TO KNOW IT WAS A *SMALL* SALT·LAKE CITY GRASS·HOPPER... HE HOPPED YOU *BLIND!*

HE USED *WINGS!* HE *USED* WINGS!

SO DO *YOU*... IN THE *BAYOU.!* WATER WINGS!

CHAPTER
15

A Bass Baritoon,
A Contraltor And
A Treble Cleft Palate

98

I TOLE POGO HERE 'BOUT YOU HAD A SINGIN' TRIO.....FLIM, FLAM AN' FLO....

YEP, THE *THREE* LOU'SIANA PERCHES.

A BASS BARITOON...A CONTRALTOR, AN'A TREBLE CLEFT PALATE.

FLIM, FLAM AN' AN'FLO'...SIMPLY SPLENDIFEROUS STELLAR STARRED *SQUAMOSE* SONGSTERS. STICK YO' HEAD IN, FRIEND.

DID YOU *HEAR'EM?* SONGBIRDS OF THE DEPTHS PRACTICIN' A NEW *ROUSER*... "ASLOOP IN THE DOOP."...LIKE IT?

GLOOP!

TRYIN' TO LISTEN TO YO' SONGFISHES UNDER THE WATER IS *RISKY* AN' *SOGGY*.

HOW RISKY?

LEAVIN' MY *EARS* OPEN THAT WAY, I IS LIKELY TO GIT WATER ON THE *BRAIN*.

WELL,YO' *TURTLE* FRIEND CAN'T GIT *WATER* ON NO BRAIN.

100

101

104

WE'RE THINKIN' OF GETTIN' UP A *PURSE,* POGO, TO GIVE TO *ROOGEY BATOON* FOR HIS *PERCHES* WE ATE.

YEP, WE'RE GONNA SELL A *JOKE* TO ONE OF THEM *FUNNY* MAGAZINES.

THEN WE'LL GIVE THE MONEY TO *ROOGEY...* WE'LL DRAW A PICTURE OF A BIG *RADIO* AND *TEEVY WRITERS'* MEETING.....

EVER'BODY IS LI'L' *CLOCKWORK MENS..* ONE OF 'EM IS GITTIN' *WOUND* BY ANOTHER WHO IS GOT THE *KEY* IN THIS GUY'S *EAR...* AN' HE IS SAYIN'....

HOL' YO'SELF IN NOW, POGO.

WHOO OO-HEE.

YOOH-HA--*OOF-HAW--*HEE... AN' HE IS SAYIN': "*I KNEW WE WAS GITTIN'* MECHANICAL BUT I DIN'T KNOW WE WOULD *WIND UP* LIKE *THIS!*" AW--HAWE--WAH-HA-- WHEE---HOO *BOY!*

YEE HAW YEOW!!

OO-- IT'S SUREFIRE!

CHAPTER
16

The Bite
Of The
Remedy

108

109

C'MON, SNAVELY...THERE'S A CUSTOMER OUT HERE. HE WANTS YOU TO PUT THE *BITE* ON HIM.

I *DO NOT!*

S'ALL RIGHT, FRIEND... I AIN'T HONGRY NO WAYS. *HAPPY* NEW YEAR AN' NO HARD FEELIN'S.

I GOT A FEELIN', SNAVELY, THAT YOU IS CONSUMED *ALL* THE SNAKE-BITE REMEDY. I'LL RULE YOU OFF THE TURF FOR *LIFE*....WHERE'S YOUR ASSISTANT?

THE APPRENTICE COBRA? HE'S LEARNIN' TO RATTLE.

IS *THIS* THE BOY YOU HIRED? HE'S NOTHIN' BUT A *ANGLE-WORM!* WHERE'S HIS *TEETH?*

ON THE END *YOU'RE* LOOKIN' AT, CHIEF, *MIGHTY MIGHTY FEW* OF US GOT TEETH.

GREAT NEWS! I'VE SECURED TWO LOWERS ON A *FREIGHT* LEAVIN' FOR *BATON ROUGE!*

JES' ABOUT IN TIME TOO...I IS BEEN *SORE TRIED* LATELY.

ME AN' THE *APPRENTICE COBRA* HERE WILL STICK A-ROUND....I'M NOT BEIN' CHASED BY *NO* RAILWAY *POL*ICE AGAIN.

NATURAL, *YOU'LL* WANT TO **THANK** ME, AFORE I LEAVES FER GIVIN' YOU A **START** OUT HERE, WON'T YOU?

NO, BUT I'LL GIVE YOU A START *BACK*. JES' BEND OVER AN' I'LL.....

HOW SHARPER THAN A CHILE'S TOOTH TO HAVE A THANKLESS SERPENT.

IF YOUSE IS RUNNIN' FOR THE *EXPRESS* IT LEFT EARLY *YESTERDAY.*

WHAT *FOR?* WE HAD SEATS *REESERVED.*

RIGHT UNDER THE *REEFRIG-AN-ATOR* CAR.

IT **HAD** TO LEAVE YESTERDAY 'CAUSE IT'S DUE IN **FORT MUDGE** TOMORROW.

A FIVE MILE TRIP!

I *KNOW!* BUT FORT MUDGE IS HARD TO FIND... GOIN' CROST-COUNTRY 'SPECIALLY.

WHAT TRAIN DON'T GO CROSS-COUNTRY?

WITHOUT TRACKS?

111

TELL YOU WHAT, FRIENDS... I'LL LOAN YOU THE BORRY OF THIS *RUNABOUT*...IT'LL GIT YOU TO *RED STICK*.

THE HON. DAN FITZPATRICK

WELL, I'M WILLIN' TO BORRY THE LOAN OF THIS *SHEBANG*... HOW'S IT *RUN*?

THAT'S MOUGHTY *KIND* OF YOU, ROOGEY. JES' GRAB A HOLT ON THEM *OARS*.

WHAT!? ME ROW ALL THE WAY TO *EAST BATON ROUGE PARISH!?*

YOU DON'T EX'PECK YO' LI'L' *FROG* FRIEND TO DO THE ROWIN'?

WULL....I AIN'T GONE DO ALL THE *WHOLE* WORK!

WHY NOT *FLY*, ROOGEY? IT'D BE *EASY*...NICE AN' COOL...GOOD VIEW...NO OARS.

RIGHT! A EXCELLENT *IDEA!*

I'LL GIVE IT A TRY...*THO' SOMETHIN'S WRONG WITH THIS IDEA, TOO.*

WE'LL TALK IT OVER WHEN WE GIT THERE.

NOT EN ROUTE, THO'...NOT EN-ROUTE.

CHAPTER
17

A Mouse Traps
And Trips

WHO'S THE TAD WITH THE BABY RATTLE, SNAVELY?

A ANGLE WORM SCAPER WHAT I PICKED UP IN *WESTWEGO*---- WANTS TO LEARN SNAKIN' AND SERPENTIN'...

HE WANTS TO BE A *RATTLER*, I S'POSE?

NO.....HE SAYS IT MAKES HIM SHAKEY HEARIN' THINGS RATTLE AHIND OF HIM ---BUT HE'S GOTTA LEARN *ALL* BRANCHES ...

WHEN HE'S THRU WITH *THIS* STEP HE GOTTA TRY BEIN' A *ADDER* THO' HIS MA SAY HE'S WEAK ON 'RITHME*TICKS* AN' STUFF -----AN' AFTER *THAT* HE GITS A TRY AS A APPRENTICE *COBRA.*

HOODED?

SHUCKS NO! HE AIN'T SHAMED OF BEIN' A *SNAKE!* HE GONE COME RIGHT OUT WITH IT---- *ACTUAL HE'D MAKE A NICE HOOP SNAKE* BUT THEY IS BEEN RULED *MYTH-OLOGICAL BEASTS* AN' IS DISQUALIFIED IN ALL STATES EAST OF THE ROCKIES.

NOW IF YOU'LL JES' HOLD THAT AN' *FINGER* THE HOLES, I'LL BLOW THE APPRENTICE COBRA A FEW CHORUSES OF RIMSKY KORSA- KOFF AN' LEARN HIM A JIG.

RIGHTO, SNAVELY.

SNAVELY, YOU IS BLOWIN' MORE *ANNIE LAURIE* AN' THE KID IS DOIN' THE *HIGHLAND FLING!*

115

116

117

NEVER PICK ON **NO**BODY *UNDER* YO' OWN SIZE, MR. MOUSE... IF YOU *WINS* YOU IS A **BULLY** AN' IF YOU *LOSES* YOU IS A **BUM**!

BUT... MIZ BEAVER, I...I...UH...

FIGHT *BIGGER* FELLAS... WIN OR LOSE, YOU IS A *HERO*. HERE, I'LL HELP YOU PICK THEM THINGS.

I WAS *ONLY* TRY AN' TO TEACH THE *YOUNG COBRA* HOW TO **THROW** A *MONGOOSE*.

MY SAKES, YOU IS PICKED QUITE A **SACKFUL**.. MIND TOTIN' 'EM FOR ME? THEY IS FER A *BEAUTIFUL* YOUNG LADY... DOWN THE LINE A PIECE.

OH? WHO?

GIRL WHAT GO BY NAME *MIZ BEAVER*, A THOUGHTFUL TYPE OF HIGH CLASS BEAUTY.

MMPH ... SNFF.. AW, YOU SHOULDNTNA DIN IT. GOIN' TO ALL THIS TROUBLE, MR. MOUSE.

JUS' SET A SPELL MR. MOUSE...I'M GOIN' INSIDE AN' SEE WHAT'S FER SUPPER.

DON'T MIND IFFEN I DO, MA'AM.

HEPZIBAH, HONEY, A SWEET TALKIN' MAN IS OUTSIDE WHAT HE IS SAY THE *NICEST* THINGS I IS *EVER* HEAR!

HE SAY HE ARE IN LOVES OF YOU, NO?

119

WOMAN TALKS 'BOUT EATIN'A *CHOCOLATE MOUSSE*, A MAN IN **MY** POSITION CAN'T BE *TOO* CAREFUL.

HATE TO RUN OFF FROM MIZ **BEAVER**... BUT.. *OH*-- *HEH*LO, MIZ BEAVER.

I BEEN SETTIN' HERE... CUT THRU TH' BACK WAY... HOPE TO *PER*SUADE YOU TO COME BACK..

YOU AIN'T THE CHOCOLATE MOUSSE WE HAD IN MIND ...*ALL A BIG MISTAKE*-- I BEEN PLAYIN'A GAME A-WAITIN' FOR YOU:

HE LOVE ME. *BANG!*

HE LOVE ME NOT. *BANG!*

HE LOVE ME. *BANG!*

WELL WELL WELL WELL WELL WELL WELL WELL WELL A MISTAKE EH WELL WELL WELL WELL WELL WELL WELL

WELL

WELL

WELL

WELL

WELL

YOU KIN SAY *THAT* A-GAIN.

WELL WELL WELL WELL WELL WELL WELL WELL

CHAPTER
18

Who Is Now And Ever
Has Been A Member
Of The Tea Party?

EVENIN', MIZ MA'M'SELLE HEPZIBAH.... EVENIN', MIZ BEAVER......HEY, MOUSE.

WELCOME TO THESE *SOIRÉE*, M'SIEUR POGO.

YOU'RE JES' IN TIME FER THE REST OF MY STORY 'BOUT *FRANCE*, POGO. PULL UP A CHAIR....

THIS FELLA I RUN INTO HIS ROOM OF, TURNS OUT TO BE A BIG *PER-FUME* MAKER (*THEY PRONOUNCES IT PARAFINE*) WELL, I GIVE HIM A IDEA.. A PERFUME LIKE A BREEZE ..OPEN SPACES... FRESH AIR... FOR THE *NONCE* CALL IT "X":

HE IS *NATURUL DEE*LIGHTED AN' IS COUNTIN' OUT A MILLION IN ONES FOR ME WHEN I MENTIONS A GOOD SLOGAN: *USE "X" AND SMELL LIKE ALL OUTDOORS*. ...WELL, RIGHT THEN A VERY NASTY THING HAPPENS, HE....

HE USED TO TELL THIS'N ABOUT *LOS ANGELES* WHEN *THAT* WAS A *TONEY* TOWN.

OH, HOW *GAY!* THAT YEAR IN *FRANCE* WAS JUST AFORE THE *BOTTOM* FELL OUT OF THE *MARKET*. I WAS WORKIN' IN THIS FOODSTUFFS EMPORIUM ON THE *RAVIOLI* WHEN I....

YOU MEAN ON THE *RIVIERA*, NO, M'SIEUR ?

WELL, IF YOU MUST GIVE IT THE *FRENCH* PRONOUNCEMENT..*O.K.* ANYHOW, *THERE I WAS ON THIS BIG PILE OF CANNED RIVIERA*....

THE **CAT**, WHOM IT WAS **MY** DUTY TO BE CHASED BY, CAME ALONG *SNEERIN'* IN THE MOTHER TONGUE, SO I HOLLERS OUT: "*CAMEMBERT!*" (FRENCH FOR "COME ON, BERT." THE CAT'S NAME BEIN' *BERTRAM*) WELL, SIR, THAT CAT GIV A LEAP.. **WOW.!**

OVER WENT THE PILE OF RIVIERA IN A *AWFUL* CRASH ..... THE FLOOR SAGGED, QUIVERED, AN' *BOOM! THE BOTTOM FELL OUT OF THE MARKET!* WE ALL LANDED IN THE CELLAR SCREAMIN' GALLICISMS WHICH BRING THE GENDARMES ON THE DOUBLE AN'......

HOW 'BOUT "LIZA JANE"?

STOP ME IF I'M **BORIN'** YOU BUT IT'S SUCH A CLEAR NIGHT FOR A GOOD TALK... WELL, WHEN THAT MARKET ON THE RUE DE LA CHAT COLLAPSED IT CAUSED QUITE A **STIR**...1929 IT WAS...

THE PAPERS WERE FULL OF IT.. PEOPLE SAID: *WHY'D THE BOTTOM FALL OUT OF THE MARKET?"* HA.! I KNOW.! THE CAT KNOCKED OVER THE CANNED GOODS. *DID THE EXPERTS ASK ME?* **NO**, THEY..

THEY **MIGHT** OF BEEN THINKIN' OF ANOTHER MARKET.

Y'MEAN ANOTHER MARKET COLLAPSED THAT YEAR?

A MARKET ON *WALL STREET.*

A COINCIDENCE! WALL STREET STORE, HUH? SMALL PLACE, NO DOUBT... *NEVER HEARD OF IT.*

NO, IT HAD A LI'L' SIZE ON IT.... Y'EVER HEAR OF THIS **WALL STREET** WHAT POLITICIANS AN' **REE**VOLUTIONARY RASCALS IS ALLUS HOLLER'N' *DOWN WITH IT?*

ALWAYS THOUGHT THAT WAS A OL' MYTHOLOGICAL BEAST... WODDYA KNOW! WELL, THIS **BIG** MARKET COLLAPSE *I* WAS IN WAS ...

123

ALL EVENINGS IN THESE *PARTY,* MY *SOIRÉE, THESE* PERSON IS SHOOT OFF *MOUSE TRAP* AN' IS *LONG DRAW* OUT THE BOW.

HE'S *MY* GENNLEMAN GUEST! *AN'* IT'S AS MUCH *MY* SWARRY AS *YOURN.*

SOMETHIN' 'BOUT ME GITS WIMMEN TO FIGHTIN'

THEY IS EASY RILED.

BUT M'SIEUR LE POGO IS HERE AWAIT WITH *BANJO,* WITH MUSIC, WITH SOCIETY VERSE TO PERFORM...

SUCH AS?

ATTEND THE MENU! *SUCH AS* "CASÉE A LA BATON! *SUCH AS* "LE BEAU PIPP!" *SUCH AS* "MOE LE BRANNIGAN!" *THAT* IS WHAT IS SUCH AS.

MOLLY BRAN... ...*AGAIN?* US HEARN THAT *TWO YEARS RUNNIN'!*

YOU DO NO LIKE?

THAT'S *EX'ACK* WHY WE WAS RUNNIN', HONEY. MOLLY OUGHTA *SUE* SOMEBODY.

ALLUS THUNK MY *LOUD* *BANJO* WORK COVERED MY VOICE PERTY GOOD.

WELL... YES AN' NO.

IN-AN-ASMUCH AS THE *SOIRÉE* IS BOGGED INTO A VERITABOBBLE *SAR-GASSO,* POGO AN' I GONE CHEER UP US.

YUP... PORKYPINE IS RUNNED ACROSS A NEW TUNE .... IT GOT A LOTTA *ZIP* IN IT SO TO SPEAK ...

I'LL ROUSE AHEAD WITH THE SOPRANO WORDS WHILST YOU FOLLY 'LONG WITH THE *BOOM A DIDDY BOOM!*

FOLLY IT IS.

125

126

OKAY! *OKAY!* HIT THAT "SIGHT" HARDER..... OTHER WISE, *SOLID!* Y'KNOW I WAS TALKIN' ABOUT THE *PARTY* TO OL' *TROTSKY* YESTIDDY AN' HE SAY, "THIS IS GOTTA BE *BLOWED UP GOOD.*"

TROTSKY?

YEH... HIM WITH THE SIX PIECE BAND... *TURKEY TROTSKY* AND HIS *DIXIE GYPSIES* ..... HE SAY A BLUE NOTE GOTTA BE BLEW BUT *SOLID!*

OH, SURE! SOLID BLUE IS MY OWN FAVORITE SHADE.

AS WE QUIETLY TAKE *POGO'S* GRUB, (HE BEING AWAY FROM HOME LIKE THE IRRESPONSIBLE DESPOTIC LANDLORD HE IS,) *I WORRY....*

YEAH.

PENSACOLA IT'S THE SPA

I WORRY ABOUT A WORLD WHERE AN HONEST MAN NEVER KNOWS *WHO* IT IS SAFE TO BE *AGAINST.* ONLY YESTER-DAY I TRUSTED THE TURTLE... WE'D TURNED TO HIS SIDE .....IN FACT, *JOINED 'EM!*

YEAH.

WE KNEW OF HIS *STRATIFIED STUPIDISM*...WE WERE *SURE*: HERE WAS ONE WE COULD BE AGAINST WITH *IMPLINISTIC SECURITISM!* WHAT HAPPENS? HE REVEALS HIS TRUE FACE ..... *HE HAS POWERFUL FRIENDS!* WHO CAN BE TRUSTED?

YEAH.

STOP LOOKIN' AT ME LIKE THAT.

YEAH.

CHAPTER
19

A Fall Classic
Is Felled

129

OH, MIZ BEAVER

YOO HOO ♪♫

HMPH! AIN'T YOU GOT NOTHIN' IN A MORE DAINTY SIZE --- 'BOUT A **NINE**, MEBBE?

UMPIRE

HOPE YOU DON'T MIND ME *PRAC-TICIN'* MY **RADIO JOB**, UNCLE BALD-WIN ---'TAINT HOOKED UP YET, BUT.... HERE GOES : *GOOD AFTERNOON, HERE IS A IMPORTANT PRE-GAME FLASH!*

SEE IT *NOW!* THE **THROBBING NEW FILM** *"CUMQUAT BLOSSOMS"* SEE THE *ALLURIN'* **MIBSIE FARQUHAR**, THE CURVACEOUS AN' *DEE-LECTABLE* **TOO-TOO DEVINE** ---*AND* THAT SLOW BURNIN' *TIGRESS*, GREEN-EYED *FOLLY FRISBIE!*

131

132

WHY AIN'T YOU LETTIN' LI'L' *GRUN-DOON* PLAY IN YO' **WORLD SERIES** NO MORE?

IT'S *OVER*... HE **UN**RAVELED OUR **BALL.**

IF YOU AIN'T GONE LET HIM PLAY YOU OUGHT TO GIVE BACK HIM HIS BALL.

HE MADE A **HOO-RAW'S NEST** OUTEN IT.

AN' IT *WASN'T* HIS ANYHOWS... HE JES' TRY TO SWAP OFF'N HIS BIG 'UN FER IT.

IF YOU AIN'T GONE LET HIM PLAY WE'LL JES' TAKE THE *BIG* ONE TOO.

I'M SORRY WE EVER LAID A *EYE* ON YO' LI'L' SCAPER.

IF YOU AIN'T GONE LET HIM PLAY THEY'S NO REQUIRE TO *APOLOGY,* MR. ALBERT. US GROUN'CHUNKS KIN TAKE A *HINT!*

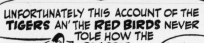

UNFORTUNATELY THIS ACCOUNT OF THE **TIGERS** AN' THE **RED BIRDS** NEVER TOLE HOW THE **CLASSIC ENDED.**

DIN'T YOU GIT THE NEXT DAY'S PAPER?

WELL, *I TRIED*... BUT SOMETHIN' HAPPENED TO THE *FREEDOM* OF THE *PRESS*...

WHAT!? OUR NEWSPAPERS IS BOUND BY THE RED BLOODED PRINTERS' INK WHAT COURSES THRU THEIR VEINS TO...

HEAR! HEAR!

NOT THAT...I MEAN THE *FIRST* DAY I GOT A *FREE* PAPER WHEN THE NEWSBOY IN **CHICAGO** WAS.. *(I WAS AT THE FAIR AT THE TIME)* WHEN HE WAS LOOKIN' AT A BALLOON.

BUT THE *NEXT DAY* THIS FERRET SPOTS ME AN' HE SCREAMS AFTER ME DOWN MICHIGAN BOULEVARD..... *HAH!* THE *CROWDS!* YOU'D THINK THEY NEVER SAW A TIGER SWIPE A NEWSPAPER BEFORE ....

NO, I NEVER *DID* FIND OUT HOW BADLY WE BEAT THE *RED BIRDS* THAT YEAR ... FOR ME, FREEDOM OF THE *PRESS* ENDED WHEN...

THE **GENDARMES** INTERFERED AN' I AIN'T HAD A **FREE** PAPER SINCE... SOMETHING ABOUT ME ALERTS THE MOST NUMP-BRAINED NEWSBOY... *HOWEVER,* THE TRASH BASKETS I'VE BROWSED THRU LATELY *ALL* INDICATE THE PRESS HAS *CLAMPED DOWN!*

WHERE?

WHERE?! HA?! DO WE HAVE HEADLINES LIKE *THIS* ANYMORE? MY *FAVORITE* KIND?...*NO!* THEY *BURY* THINGS!

PAPERS PRINT THE NEWS WHAT *IS*...NOT JES' WHAT YOU *WANTS.* WODDYA MEAN THEY *BURY* THINGS?

TIGERS WIN 1934 FLAG

HERE'S A PAPER (*WRAPPED 'ROUND A FISH*) AUG. 29 1953. *BURY THINGS?!* LOOK WHERE THEY PUT *DETROIT* IN THE STANDIN'S...*SEVENTH PLACE!* 40 GAMES BURIED! THAT DIDN'T HAPPEN IN *MY* DAY, FRIENDS!

IT'S *MY* CONTENTION, FRIENDS, IF WE HAD A *TRULY* LIBERAL PRESS THE *TIGERS* WOULD OF GOT A BETTER SPOT IN THE *AMERICAN LEAGUE STANDINGS*...SUCH THINGS ARE NOT THE WHIM OF CHANCE....

THEY IS THE *WHIM* OF WHAMMY.

OL' ROY MATSON

FORGET SPORTS...*TAKE THEM COMICKAL* STRIPS...A NEWS PAPER BUYS A STRIP AN' WILL IT LET OTHER PAPERS IN THE SAME TOWN HAVE IT, TOO?

HA! TALK ABOUT FREEDOM.

ROY MATSON

BESIDES.... WHO..*WHAT* PITIFUL PIT-TANCE READS THE PAPERS TODAY?

WELL, THERE'S A WAY OVER 50,000,000 COPIES EVER'DAY READ BY, AT THE VERY LEAST, TWO PEOPLE APIECE.

WELL, YOU DON'T HAVE TO **SNAP** MY HEAD OFF.

DIN'T KNOW IT WAS MADE OF RUBBER, SON.

HUMPH!

LAST TIME A PAPER MENTIONED ME THEY SPELT MY NAME WRONG.

SEE, YOU IS FUSSIN' 'BOUT A FREE PRESS AN' THE MINUTE THEY MAKES **FREE** WITH YO' NAME, YOU GITS **MAD.**

CRITTURS IS **ALL** ALIKE.

WHAT MAKES YOU SO TALKY? THEM'S THE **FIRST** WORDS YOU SAID SINCE **WENSDAY.**

I BEEN MULLIN' AT 'EM.

NEWSPAPERS ARE PUT OUT BY CRITTURS JES' LIKE OTHER THINGS IS DID BY CRITTURS... SOMETIMES GOOD... SOMETIMES NOT SO ...BUT CONSIDERIN' THAT EVER'BODY IS GOT **TWO LEFT FEET** US CRITTURS DON'T DO BAD...

I FIGGERS, PORKY, THAT **EVERY MAN'S HEART IS EVENTUAL** IN THE **RIGHT PLACE.**

AN' I FIGGERS POGO, THAT IF A MAN'S GONNA BE **WRONG** 'BOUT SOMETHIN', **THAT** IS THE **BEST** WRONG THING TO KEEP BEIN' WRONG ABOUT, 'TIL **FOREVER.**

An Episode That
Goes Off Half Cockney

138

139

142

CHAPTER
22

A Scandal
For School

145

OL' **OWL** GONE OPEN UP A **SCHOOL,** HOUN' DOG.

GREAT NEWS! YES, **INDEED.'**

MY SCHOOL DAYS ... THE GOLDEN YEARS IN FIRST GRADE WERE GONE TOO SOON ... I'VE OFT WONDERED WHAT HAPPENED TO OUR MANUAL TRAININ' TEACHER AN' FOOTBALL COACH ..

A **GREAT** GUY, HUH?

A LADY ... MISS **BOOMBAH**.. WE LOVED HER LIKE A BROTHER...CALLED HER **"SIS"**.... WE HAD A CHEER FOR SPORTING CONTESTS..:: **YAY WILLACOOCHIE! GLORIOUS WILLACOOCHIE EVER TRUE! FIGHT ON, CHARTROOS AN' PLAID!**

WILLACOO-CHEEE! SIS **BOOMBAH."** WE **ALWAYS** TACKED **HER** ON THE **END.** SHE HOLLERED LOUDER'N ANYBODY...

I SHOULDA THUNK SHE WOULD

THIS NOW, **SCHOOL**....SOON'S I GIT ANOTHER **BENCH** MADE IT'S GONE BE A **SURE'NUFF** **U**-NIVERSITY...

GOOD FOR IT!'

I'LL HELP YOU TEACH ALL 'BOUT MY **SPECIALTY**.... BECAUSE I IS A **EXPERT** ON MY SPECIALTY..... **AN'** IS A **SPECIALIST** ON IT TOO BESIDES.

147

YOUR STUDENT BODY IS *PREE*-PARED TO GIVE YOU **TEMPORARY** UNDERPINNIN', PROF.

THEN YOU KIN GIT OVER TO YOUR **AUNTIE'S**...... *MIZ MYRTLE IS BOUND TO REMEMBER HOW* TO GIT YO' LEG BONES **OUTEN** YO' SHELL ..... **EASY NOW**....

GOT HIM...

OKAY...NORTH BY NORTH EAST-EAST BY WEST-SOUTH-WEST MEN...**BRISK!**

PHOO...MOST DANGEROUS THING I COULD GET WOULD BE **MORE** HELP LIKE **THAT**.

GOOD NEWS, OWL! **GOOD NEWS!** WE IS COMIN' OVER TO **JOIN** *YOUR* **FACULTY.**

WHOOOP! KEERFUL.

IS YOU FOLKS COMIN' TO **SCHOOL?**

YES, YES! WE'RE ACHIN' TO START...

WHERE'S THE **STADIUM?** WE GOT THE **BACKFIELD** ALL FIGGERED OUT....

NO SPORTS ALLOWED!

149

CHAPTER
23

A Form Of
Hire Education

152

153

154

155

156

CHAPTER
24

Nothing Taught
Here Fearlessly

QUICK! QUICK!

THE TEAM IS AT PRACTICE.

CAPTAIN C GLENN ADFOX

HOT DOG! I DON'T WANT TO MISS THIS! WAIT FOR ME!

YOU'RE JUST IN TIME.

I'M ALL TUNED UP ... WHERE'S THE REST OF THE TEAM?

RIGHT OVER THERE, YOUNG MAN. GET THE BEANBAG, PLEASE.

BEAN BAG!? AND A TEAM OF BIRDS! HOW CAN WE EVER FACE U.C.L.A.?

OH, THE BIRDS ARE NOT ON THE SQUAD. I HIT BEAUREGARD WITH A LOOSE SACK OF WHITE NAVIES AN' NOW HE'S ALIVE WITH COMMON GRACKLES.

I'LL BRUSH THE BIRDS AN' BEANS OFF, HOUN' DOG, AN' MEBBE YOU'LL EXPLAIN.

WELL, SIS BOOMBAH OFFERED TO COACH THE TEAM ON ACCOUNT SHE COACHED MY FIRST GRADE TO THE CHAMPEENSHIP FIVE YEAR STRAIGHT!

POOT

BUT HOW COME YOU IS COVERED WITH BEANS? WHAT WILL NOTER DAME SAY WHEN WE SHOWS UP PLAYIN' BEAN-BAG!?

164

167

WE HEARD WHAT THEY'RE PLOTTIN' IN THEM HUDDLES. *REVOLUTION!* *ANARCHY!*

THEY'RE GONNA STEAL CALIFORNIA!

'Incredible'

PHOO..WHUFFO AN' BESIDES WHERE WOULD THEY *KEEP* IT?

LET'S GO, EVER'BODY, FOR A RIDE IN THE NEW BOAT WE NAMED FOR DOCTOR CARL.

STOP BEIN' SO *BROODY*, DEACON. C'MON.

What? With these students plotting to steal California....?

BUT, AS M'SIEUR *PORK LE PINE* IS SAY: *WHERE ARE THESE CAULIFORN TO BE KEPT IF HE IS STOLING?*

DOC CARL HARTMAN

Phaugh! They'll keep it in Florida perchance or sell it in South America ~~~~~ The whole idea fills me with *Loathing*

I FEEL THE *SAME!*

YES SIR!

If you two feel like I do ~~*How* can you both look so happy?

WE'RE *ALWAYS* *HAPPY* WHEN WE'RE FILLED WITH *LOATHING.*

SURE.. AIN'T *YOU?*

WELL, I'LL BE *DOGGED!* NOT A *PEEP*, HUH?

NARY A! SO OLD PETER INVENTED SPANISH FOR SPAIN, CHINESE FOR CHINA, ENGLISH FOR THE *U.S.* AND *A* ... AND *ALL* LIKE THAT THERE...

BLESS MY SOUL.... THEN THEY COULD *ANSWER BACK* ON THE CABLE, HUH?

WELL, HE HAD TO INVENT A CODE FOR *ANSWERING*.... CALLED IT, *NATURAL*, THE *RE-MORSE* CODE....... *NEXT* THEY NEEDED ELECTRICITY, SO CZAR IVAN TOOK A KITE AND SOME STRING AND A KEY

YOU SAY THE *DEACON* IS AGAINST OUR ACTIVITIES?

SAYS HE DON'T COM-PREHEND 'EM, COACH.

COME SEE HIM, COACH BOOMBAH, AN' *WOO* THE OL' BUZZARD.

MM.. EVERY TIME I WOO A MAN HE FOLDS IN THE STRETCH. MEN HAVE NO *DE-FENSE* AND LITTLE STAMINA.

NO, I MEAN BE *NICE* TO HIM... MAKE HIM *BUSINESS MANAGER* OF THE *BEAN BAG TEAM*..... THINK HOW HAPPY HE'LL BE, COUNTIN' THE HOUSE WHEN YOU PLAY *IGLOO U.*

FROM WHAT I HEAR OF THE *DEACON* HE'S TOO LAZY TO COUNT TO *SEVEN* ON HIS FINGERS.

I *DUNNO*, MOST BUSINESS MAN-AGERS KIN BE VERY HAPPY COUNTIN' UP TO *SEVEN* OR EE-LEVEN ON THEIR HANDS AN' KNEES.

THE HON. FRED W. GIESEL

The Carols
Ground Out ...
First Bass To
Short

IT'S *ALREADY* DECEMBER SEVENTEEN...US'LL GOTTA GO *FAST* TO BE ALL SET BY THE TWENTY-FIFTH.

MAN! WHAT'S THE MATTER WITH THEM *GROWED-UPS*? *I* DON'T GIT TUNED UP IN A *RUSH!* I BEEN READY FOR 357 DAYS! *MAN AN' BOY!*

QUIET, YOU TADS. ALL RIGHT, NOW, FIRST: *"HERE WE GO A-WAFFLIN"* **HIT IT!**

GMX.

WURF.

WANG A BLANG WAM A SOCK

WODDYA THINK OF *THAT* ONE, CHURCHY?

HARD FOR ME TO SAY-- I THINK I'M *TOO CLOSE* TO IT---

HOW 'BOUT US PLAYIN' *HOOKEY* FROM CAROL PRACTICE AN' GOIN' ON A *EXPEDITION?*

YOU BOTH KNOWS THE WORDS TO THE *"TWELVE DAYS OF CHRISTMAS"* AN' ALL?

GBNX.

WURF WURF.

175

I **THOUGHT** SO... MAM SAYS **CHILLUNS** IS THE SINGLE TYPE CRITTURS WHAT IS **ALWAYS** PREE-PARED FOR CHRISTMAS... IF CHRISTMAS WAS **DECLARED** ON **FOURTH** OF **JULY**... **US** WOULD BE **READY!**

GROWED FOLKS IS THE **ONLY** ONES WHAT GOTTA PRACTICE UP GITTIN' IN THE **MOOD**... SPRING **DEC. 25** ON 'EM SUDDEN AN' **HALF** WOULDN'T HAND OUT THEIR **RIGHT NAMES.**

WHY ISN'T YOU TADS PRACTICIN' UP FOR CHRISTMAS LIKE ALL THE OTHERS?

SHUCKS, US CHILLUN IS BEEN READY **ALL** THE **WHOLE** YEAR.

READY FOR WHAT EVER COMES, HUH? Y'ALL KIN **SPELL** YO' NAME GOOD SO'S WHEN YOU SEES A PACKAGE TAGGED FOR **YOU** YOU'LL OPEN IT RIGHT QUICK...

YOU BETCHA!

AN' ALL YEAR YOU SHOWED YO' MAMS AN' PAPS, YO' UNCLES, AUNTS AN' KIN THAT THE WORLD IS REALLY A PLACE OF LOVE BY BEIN' SWEET TO 'EM... KEEPIN' 'EM AS READY FOR CHRISTMAS AS YOU IS? HELPIN' 'EM GIT THROUGH?

WELL.....

WELL.... THINK THERE'S STILL TIME TO GIVE 'EM A HAND THAT WAY, UNCLE PORKY?

AW... THERE'S **ALLUS** TIME FOR IT PROVIDIN' YOU DON'T WASTE NONE OF IT.

178

AN' SO ALL TO BED ------

DUNNO *WHY* I BOTHER WITH THIS YEAR AFTER *YEAR...* *HALLOO!* *WAKE UP!* *CHRISTMAS EVE!*

OH ... IT'S *YOU*, PORKY... DON'T YOU KNOW YOU AN' ME IS FILLED THE STOCKIN'S AN' JES' FINISH TRIMMIN' THE *TREES? IT'S FOUR A.M.*

SO ....YOU DON'T *NEED* A WATCH?

THAT'S GOOD, 'CAUSE HERE'S SOMETHIN' I BEEN SAVIN' FOR YOU SINCE *AUGUST*... NOW, PLEASE, DON'T *FAWN* ON ME.....*A SPRIG OF LOVE-IN-IDLENESS* ---'TAIN'T MUCH, **BUT,** THE WAY FOLKS TREATS EACH OTHER NOW·A·DAYS....

..IF I LEAVES THIS UP TO *ANY BODY ELSE*, *YOU'LL* BE LUCKY IF YOU RECEIVES A *SIMPLE GOOD MORNIN'!*

AW--- YOU OL' *PORKYPINE... I DO BLEEVE* I'LL WAKE UP AN' MAKE COCOA AN' *PEANER BUTTER SAN'WIGHES.*

179

One Final Word
Leads To Another

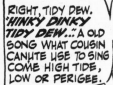

182

THIS NEW MAN YOU IS GONE BE.... *WHO IS HE?* WHO YOU GONE *BE?*

OH... MEBBE I'LL BE PRESIDENT *GRANT*...I HEAR HE GOT A BIG PLACE UP ON RIVERSIDE *DRIVE*... RENT *FREE!*

NO...THAT JOB IS BEEN DONE...YOU GOTTA BE A *BRAN'NEW* SOMEBODY.

WODDYA MEAN THE JOB'S *DONE? THERE'S STILL A DEE-*MAND.... STILL *ROOM* AT THE *TOP,* MY FRIEND.

YOU WON'T LIKE BEIN' UP ON THAT DRIVE ...TOO MANY CARS...TOO MUCH *TRAFFIC*...

THEN I COULD SET UP AS A *TRAFFIC COP.* THINK OF THE BUSINESS I'D GET!

YOU'D GET THE BUSINESS AN' YOU'D *DESERVE* IT.... *UH, HOW CAN YOU TEAR YOURSELF AWAY, POGO?*

YOU GOT A REASON TO LEAVE?

NO---- BUT I'LL THINK OF SOMETHIN'

CHURCHY BEEN TALKIN' TO *BUN RABBIT...* CLAIMIN' HE'S GONE BE A NEW MAN BUT CAN'T FIGGER WHO...

HERE HE COME... HE LOOK JES' LIKE *LAST YEAR* AN' EVEN MORE LIKE THE ONE AFORE THAT.

DID YOU AN' OL' BUN DECIDE WHO YOU'S TO BE FOR THE NEW YEAR?

I TURNED HIM OFF WITH A *OLD JEST*...TOLE HIM I IS GONE BE A *APPLE SELLER* SEEIN' AS IT MOUGHT BE A RAGE.

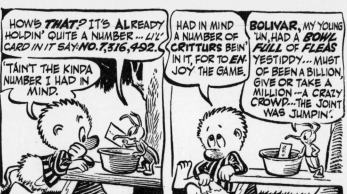

186

187

THE ESTATE

OF

OUR INDEPENDENCE

Sculling alertly through the waters of a Sunday afternoon we listen to the radio reports, hurried to our anxious ears through the driving rain, reports of drownings, highway accidents, death by design, explosions of small boys. When the clamor has died and is replaced by the soothing strains of George M. Cohan played upon organ and drum, the soft voice of man's best friend, his wife, observes: "Holiday rain. All those people died for nothing. . . . At least they might have had better weather for it."

And indeed they might have. In fact, we might all have better weather as we jostle toward the finish. Too soon we breast the tape and too late we realize the fun lay in the running. We deny that the end justifies the means without ever stopping to consider that for practical purposes the End and the Means are one and the same thing. If there is to be any satisfaction in life it must come in transit, for who can tell when he will be struck down in mid-method?

So, as we speed along, running up our colors and running down our neighbors, it might be well to avoid being hoist by our own halyards. In this Era of the Boomerang it is easy to counter suspicion with suspicion. It is not quite as easy to return hate for love but many of us manage it through the simple procedure of viewing all love with the suspicion reserved for the unknown. This is unfortunate because love takes many 189 forms, (not all of them immediately identifiable and therefore even more suspect.) One of these forms is humor.

Naturally the humorist in any age is viewed with some misgivings for he plays with no particular team. He performs the duties of a busy-body umpire who may be expected to hit, run, field the ball and call himself out on a close play at home. The fact that he may work equally well and equally often for all teams does not make him any more dependable. He is not to be trusted.

These very thoughts are highly suspicious because it has long been the cheerful habit of nearly every American to think fondly of himself as a humorist. And, with his flair for irreverence, his social impudence, his unblinking recognition of the truth, the American, by and large over the centuries, has been a humorous man.

Currently we have narrowed our formula for the joke down to a safe channel alive with harbor lights, bell buoys, constant soundings from the bow, shouted warnings from the shore, signal fires and manned life-boats. Such channeled activity can become ritual.

A form of ritualistic humor crept into the habits and ceremonies of the ancient North American Indians. These Original Americans employed at least one comic device (a sure-fire boff), that consisted of several humorists smearing and throwing dung over some selected colleague.

As humor, the act had one serious drawback in that it became impossible, eventually, to embrace the target in a show of good fellowship directly after the performance.

Another Original American is named by a less original American as the authority on Vigilantics who taught that a suspicious man should kick rapidly upon the groin of a suspect until the latter is made helpless. This provides mirth for spectator and raconteur.

All of this good fun, the smearing, the throwing, the kicking, is spoiled when the scape-goat is not a good sport. It is one of the major requirements of joke-function that the butt should either (A.) be quiet or (B.) get lost . . . if he is not already rendered dead.

The Era of the Boomerang is putting our national sense of humor to a severe test. The full import of inventing the world's most devastating weapon was not realized until we learned that the enemy, acting like cads, had swiped the secret. Having been prepared to snigger, we are not prepared to applaud; but neither should we be ready to whimper.

It is not the time for a man to demonstrate the strength of his guts with a belly-laugh, but nevertheless here is a comic situation. It is a comedy in the classic tradition, so near to tragedy that the difference is indiscernible to the participant. This classic comedy is fundamentally that of the Pompous Ass falling on his bulging behind. It is nearly always funny to the onlooker. It is seldom funny to the Pompous Ass. Like it or not, however, the joke remains . . . and it is on us.

So, as we move along, we cannot care who sings our country's songs; beneath the high notes of patriotism, we want to hear the low notes of laughter, always off-key, always true.

Jagged, imperfect and lovely, the goal lies here. This is the estate of our independence.

WALT KELLY